MANCHESTER
CITY
SONGBOOK

MANCHESTER
CITY
SONGBOOK

Sport Media

66 Manchester City has unbelievable fans who have always supported me. From the moment I joined the club it has felt like a second home. 99

– David Silva

Sport Media

MANCHESTER CITY
SONGBOOK

Produced by Trinity Mirror Sport Media

Managing Director: Steve Hanrahan
Commercial Director: Will Beedles
Executive Editor: Paul Dove
Executive Art Editor: Rick Cooke
Marketing and Commercial Manager: Claire Brown

Compiled by: David Clayton
Design & Production: Roy Gilfoyle & Adam Oldfield
Cover Design: Rick Cooke

Published in Great Britain in 2016.
Published and produced by Trinity Mirror Sport Media,
PO Box 48, L69 3EB.

ISBN: 9781910335611

Printed and bound by CPI Group (UK) Ltd, Croydon, CR0 4YY

Acknowledgements

All football fans sing songs – some better than others! The songs in this book are a collection of old and new songs created and sung by our supporters. You may come across the odd chant that has a word changed, but as this is a family book, we're sure you'll understand!

The songs that aren't included are for obvious reasons...

Foreword by Shaun Goater

When you hear the City fans sing your name, you know you are doing something right. This is a set of supporters who will stick by you through thick and thin – or as one guy said to me once – thin and thinner! Days like that, hopefully, are now gone forever.

I can't remember the first time I heard 'Feed the Goat', but I do remember the lads coming in and telling me how much they liked it. Whenever I heard it after that moment, it always gave me confidence to play my natural game because I knew the fans were with me all the way.

Maybe I wouldn't have scored as many goals as I did without that backing. Who am I kidding? I know I wouldn't! When I first arrived, I don't think either the fans or myself could ever have guessed what lay ahead and the four years I spent at Maine Road were the best days of my life.

My song took on a life of its own and became famous in its own right but there were three or four others I loved, too. I'll never forget walking off the pitch after we'd beaten United 3-1 in the last Maine Road derby and hearing the whole ground singing 'Who let the Goat out?' – a great memory.

Songs and chants are fun but they can also lift you higher and make you believe anything is possible. I think the City fans have come up with some of the best over the years and this collection proves that theory to be correct. I hope you enjoy them as much as I have and there isn't a day that goes by that I don't remember those fantastic songs about me echoing around Maine Road.

Happy days!

Shaun Goater, MBE

Introduction

all it gallows humour, self-deprecation or just an ability to take knocks squarely on the chin, but one thing is for sure, you can't keep Manchester City fans down for long.

In fact, for a club that has bounced between the leagues and even slipped 'down among the dead men' into the third tier of English football, Blues' followers have always made the best of things, stayed loyal and backed their team come what may.

And the humour has never been far away...

When City's relegation to Division Two became inevitable during the final game of the 1997/98 season, 6,000 travelling fans at Stoke began to sing "Are you watching Macclesfield?" as thoughts turned to some of English football's least hospitable outposts. It was funny, off the cuff and spoke volumes for the supporters who have become synonymous with seeing the lighter side of life.

No matter what, they were sticking with their team and when others would have deserted in droves, City's crowds actually increased!

The songs remained tinged with irony and opposition taunts of 'You're not famous any more' would invariably draw some witty response such as the chant at Grimsby that suggested they only sang when they were fishing.

Introduction

Whether it was thousands of voices in unison singing on a packed Kippax terrace at Maine Road or a rousing chorus of Blue Moon at the Etihad Stadium, the City fans revelled in their role as the twelfth man and that's why the chant from opposing supporters of 'Where were you when you were (erm, not so good!)' – or words to that effect – hold little weight in football. Everyone knows City fans have stuck by their team no matter what, shaping a collective body into perhaps one of the most inventive followings in the country. Of course, things have improved somewhat in the past few years and success has brought a collection of new songs.

From unforgettable chants like 'Feed The Goat And He Will Score', to 'Niall Quinn's Disco Pants', The Manchester City Songbook is the first complete collection of the chants and songs that have lifted the players or brought a smile to the faces of thousands at times when it was needed the most.

The song lyrics are invented by supporters and their reproduction here is intended to entertain and not meant to cause offence.

Enjoy!

66 I like the song the City fans sing for me –
it's original, too! In Argentina, it was 'Aguero,
Aguero'; while in Spain they chanted 'Kun,
Kun, Kun...' And now it's the 'Sergio, Sergio'
– that was all that had been missing. I like how
the City fans say it – it's pronounced 'SEHR-
hee-oh' in Spanish, and it's fun to hear the
Mancunians' 'SEHR-gee-o.' I know the fans can
come up with new songs on their own and I'll
always welcome any new ones! 99

– Sergio Aguero

Adebayor, Emmanuel
(To the tune of Sloop John B)

Adebayor, Adebayor,
He cost less than Berbatov,
He scores a lot more.

*(With Emmanuel Adebayor insulted by almost every
visiting team with varying versions of the same song, City
fans invented their own, more Ade-friendly version)*

Aguero, Sergio I

Sergio, Sergio,
Sergio, Sergio.
Sergio, Sergio,
Sergio, Sergio!

Aguero, Sergio II
(To the tune of Volare)

Aguero, whoa-oh, Aguero, whoa-oh,

He is an Argentine,

He scored in Fergie time!

*(First heard at the Manchester Senior Cup final
a few days after the Blues' title triumph in 2012)*

Aguero, Sergio III
(To the tune of La Bamba)

Kun Aguero, Aguero,

Kun Aguero, Aguero,

He scores for fun, his name is Kun, he scores for fun,

Kun, Kun Aguero,

Kun, Kun Aguero!

Aguero, Sergio IV
(To the tune of The Ants Go Marching)

The hand of God wanted him to join,
Aguero! Aguero!
He didn't just join us for some coin,
Aguero! Aguero!
We bought the lad from sunny Spain,
He gets the ball we score again,
Sergio Aguero rising us to fame!

Aguero, Sergio V
(To the tune of That's Amore)

When the ball hits the net, it's a pretty safe bet,
It's Aguero!
When your full-back's confused and defence over-used,
That's Aguero!
With the ball at his feet and the movement so sweet,
That's Aguero!
He's admired wide and far, scored against QPR,
That's Aguero!

Alan I
(To the tune of Go West)

Stand up, if you love Alan,
Stand up, if you love Alan,
Stand up, if you love Alan,
Stand up, if you love Alan!

*(City fans reacted quickly when Red Bull Salzburg brought on a sub
simply named 'Alan' during a Europa League group stage match at the
Etihad Stadium. It led to a raft of songs aimed at the bemused Brazilian
– all affectionate – as the Blues coasted to victory in the snow)*

Alan II

We love you Alan, we do!
We love you Alan, we do!
We love you Alan, we do!
Oh Alan we love you!

Allen, Clive

One Clive Allen,
There's only one Clive Allen,
One Clive Allen.
There's only one Clive Allen!

(Clive Allen became a cult figure among the City fans during his time with the club. A natural goal-scorer, he fell out with manager Peter Reid but still had the backing of the fans – until he was eventually moved on)

Anelka, Nicolas I
(To the tune of Skip To My Lou)

Super, super Nic,
Super, super Nic,
Super, super Nic,
Super Nic Anelka.

Anelka, Nicolas II
(To the tune of Bread Of Heaven)

Feed the Elk,
Feed the Elk,
Feed the Elk and he will score,
Feed the Elk and he will score!

(A play on the 'Feed the Goat' chant, Anelka remained at City after strike partner Shaun Goater and inherited the song for a short time)

Argentinian Blues

We've got Nicolas Otamendi,
We've got Kun Aguero too,
We've got Pablo Zabaleta,
They're our Argentinian Blues.
Our Argentinian Blues are coming after you,
Our Argies are coming after you!
We've got Martin Demichelis.
We've got Zuculini too,
We've got Willy Caballero,
They're our Argentinian Blues,
Our Argentinian Blues are coming after you,
Our Argies are coming after you!

Balotelli, Mario

Oh Balotelli he's a striker…
He's good at darts,
He's allergic to the grass but when he
plays the lad is class,
Drives around Moss Side with a wallet full of cash,
Can't put on his vest,
but when he does he is the best
Goes into schools and tells teachers all the rules
Oh Balotelli,
He's a striker,
He's good at darts…

(Cult Italian striker Mario Balotelli attracted more headlines than any other during his relatively short time with City. The stories continued unabated until there was enough material to come up with one of the most popular City songs since 'Feed the Goat', encapsulating all his alleged escapades into one, clever, affectionate tribute)

Balotelli, Mario II

(To the tune of the White Stripes' Seven Nations Army)

Mario Bal-o-telli,
Mario Bal-o-telli!

Bananas!

Bananas, bananas, bananas!

*(Sung during City's inflatable craze in the late 1980s
– simple and straight to the point)*

Barry, Gareth
(To the tune of My Old Man's A Dustman)

Gareth Barry is magic,
He wears a magic hat,
And when he saw the blue camp,
He said "I'm havin' that."

He didn't go to Anfield,
Or sign for Arsenal,
He joined the super City,
Because we are wonderful...

*(Having turned down Liverpool and Arsenal, Gareth Barry
was subjected to heckling whenever he played any of the clubs
mentioned – the City fans respond with the above song...)*

Bell, Colin – Colin The King
(To the tune of Lily The Pink)

We'll drink a drink, a drink,
To Colin the king, the king, the king,
'Cos he's the saviour of Man City,
He's the greatest inside forward that the world
has ever seen!

*(One of the oldest songs City fans still sing, 'Colin the King'
is now only aired on special occasions and always started
with an elongated 'Weeeeeee'lllll' when the
chorus is repeated)*

Bell, Colin II
(To the tune of Yellow Submarine)

Number one, is Colin Bell,
Number two, is Colin Bell,
Number three, is Colin Bell,
Number four, is Colin Bell,
Number five, is Colin Bell,
Number six, is Colin Bell,
Number seven, is Colin Bell,
Number eight, is Colin Bell,
Number nine, is Colin Bell,
Number ten, is Colin Bell,
Number eleven, is Colin Bell,
The substitute is Colin Bell,
The referee is Colin Bell,
The man who sells the pies is Colin Bell.

We all live in a Colin Bell world,
A Colin Bell world,
A Colin Bell world.
We all live in a Colin Bell world,
A Colin Bell world,
A Colin Bell world!

*(The message that Colin Bell WAS the City team for the
best part of a decade is rarely heard these days)*

Bell, Colin III
(To the tune of My Old Man's A Dustman)

His name is Colin Bell,
From Bury he did come,
He plays for old Joe Mercer's team,
That's in Division One.

And when you walk down Maine Road,
You'll always hear the cry,
We are the best team in the land,
That no-one can deny.

Bell, Lee And Summerbee

Heigh ho, heigh ho, we're off to Mexico,
With Bell and Lee and Summerbee,
Heigh ho, heigh ho...
Heigh ho, heigh ho, we're off to Mexico,
With Bell and Lee and Summerbee,
Heigh ho, heigh ho...

*(In tribute to City's potential England 1970
World Cup stars)*

Bellamy, Craig

Bellamy, Bellamy!
Bellamy, Bellamy!

Benarbia, Ali
(To the tune of Hey, Baby!)

Hey, Ali Ben-arbia,
Ooh-ah!
I wanna kno-o-o-ow,
Will you feed the Goat?

(Sung to the Algerian genius who had more assists in one season than any other City player in living memory during the 2001/02 season – as the song suggests, Shaun Goater was fed often with Ali B behind him!)

Benjani
(To the tune of Volare)

Benjani woah-oh, Benjani woah-oh,
He comes from Zimbabwe,
He scored on derby day...

*(Benjani became an instant crowd favourite by scoring on
his debut for City away to United and helping the Blues
record a first Old Trafford win for 34 years)*

Berkovic, Eyal
(To the tune of Go West)

Eyal, Eyal Berk-o-vic,
Eyal, Eyal Berk-o-vic
Eyal, Eyal Berk-o-vic
Eyal, Eyal Berk-o-vic!

Best Team In The World...

City, City,
The best team in the land,
In all the world (in all the world).

*(An old favourite that has stood the test of time and is
still heard at the Etihad Stadium today)*

Bless Them All

Bless 'em all, bless 'em all,
Bert Trautmann, Dave Ewing and Paul.
Bless Roy Little who blocks out the wing,
Bless Jack Dyson the penalty king.
And with Leivers and Spurdle so tall,
And Johnstone, the Prince of them all.
Come on the light Blues,
It's always the right blue,
So cheer up me lads,
Bless 'em all.

*(And old song sang back in the 1960s when the wit and
wisdom of the terraces wasn't quite what it is today)*

Blue Moon – United

Blue Moon,
You started singing our tune,
You won't be singing for long,
'Cause we still beat you 5-1.

*(When United fans sang that City fans had celebrated too soon
having led 2-0 at half-time in a Maine Road derby, only to lose
3-2, the response was to remind Reds' fans that they'd still taken
a beating not that long ago)*

Blue Wembley
(To the tune of White Christmas)

I'm dreaming of a Blue Wembley,
Just like the ones I used to know,
There'll be blue flags flying,
And Reds fans crying,
To see, City win the cup (win the cup!).

(Sung on the run to the 1981 FA Cup Final and for several years after, the City fans' version of Irving Berlin's 'White Christmas' serenaded the Blues during FA Cup runs for around a decade. Always nice to hear when there's snow in the air and enjoyed something of a revival during City's 2011 FA Cup run which ended in a 1-0 final win over Stoke)

Blue Moon

Blue Moon,
You saw me standing alone,
Without a dream in my heart,
Without a love of my own.

Blue Moon,
You saw me standing alone,
Without a dream in my heart,
Without a love of my own.

(Blue Moon is rumoured to have started during an away game at Anfield in 1989, but as with anything as ambiguous as when a song actually began to be sung by the masses, it's no more than an educated guess. Though Blue Moon has also been sung by fans of Peterborough United and Crewe, it became associated with City as it began to be heard at every home game throughout the 1990s until the present day when the song cannot be played or sung by anyone else without the association to City)

Bond, John

We're on the march, we're John Bond's army,
We're all going to Wembley,
And we'll really shake 'em up,
When we win the FA Cup,
'Cos City are the greatest football team.

*(John Bond arrived in 1980 and transformed a team
threatened with relegation into the 1981 FA Cup finalists)*

Born In Gorton
(To the tune of Matchstick Men)

We were born in Gorton,
Then we moved to Moss Side,
From there our name spread far and wide.
Everybody's seen the Sky Blue shirt.

From old aged men with hair like snow,
To five-year-olds, with beds to go,
Standing side by side as they watch their team
with pride.

And people ask you who you support,
And you tell 'em, but you don't know why,
It doesn't matter if they win or lose,
Just as long as they try.

No Man U or Arsenal for me,
It's Bell, Lee, Summerbee,
I'll be a Kippax Kid, until the day I die.

Boyata, Dedryck

Dedryckkkkkkkkkk!
Boyata, Boyata!
Boyata, Boyata!
Boyata, Boyata!

The Boys In Blue

City! Manchester City!
We are the lads who are playing to win,
City - the Boys in Blue will never give in!
Football is the game that we all live for,
Saturday is the day we play the game,
Everybody has to pull together,
And together we will stand.
Even if we're playing down at Maine Road,
Or if we play a million miles away,
There will always be our loyal fans behind us,
To cheer us on our way!
City! Manchester City!
We are the lads who are playing to win,
City – the Boys in Blue will never give in.
Blue and white we play together,
We will carry on forever more!
Maybe in another generation,
When other lads have come to take our place,
They'll carry on the glory of the City,
Keeping City in the place.
City! Manchester City!

We are the lads who are playing to win,
City – the Boys in Blue will never give in,
The Boys in Blue will never give in,
The Boys in Blue will never give in!

*(An original song written by half of the 1970s band 10cc
and sang by the City squad of the day, 'The Boys in Blue'
was recorded in the early 1970s and became the song the
team ran out to for more than 20 years at Maine Road.
Occasionally sung by the supporters and occasionally played
at the City of Manchester Stadium, the song has its place in
the club's history and hearts)*

Brown, Michael
(To the tune of Knees Up Mother Brown)

Knees up Michael Brown,
Knees up Michael Brown,
Get those knees up, knees up, knees up,
Knees up Michael Brown!

*(Sang in honour of City's tough-tackling Academy graduate
Michael Brown who, shall we say, tackled
enthusiastically on occasion)*

Caballero, Willy I
(To the tune of Yellow Submarine)

City won the cup with a Willy in the goal,
A Willy in the goal, a Willy in the goal,
a Willy in the goal
City won the cup with a Willy in the goal,
A Willy in the goal, a Willy in the goal
(Repeat until bored)

*(Sung in honour of Capital One Cup penalty shoot-out hero
Willy Caballero in 2016)*

Caballero, Willy II
(To the tune of Do The Hokey Cokey)

You put your Willy in,
Your Willy out,
In, out, in, out, you shake it all about,
You do the Caballero and you turn around,
That's what it's all about.
Oh, Willy Caballero!
Oh, Willy Caballero!
Oh, Willy Caballero!
In, out, in, out, you shake it all about

Castillo, Nery
(To the tune of Volare)

Castillo...whoah oh-oh!
Castillo...whoah oh-oh!
He paid his transfer fee,
To sign for Man City!

*(Then cash-strapped City signed a collection of journeymen strikers,
free agents and loan players during the leaner pre-Abu Dhabi days
and rumours that Nery Castillo had actually paid part of the fee that
allowed him to the Blues resulted in the above song)*

Christmas Shopping
(To the tune of Guantanamera)

Gone Christmas shopping,
You should have gone Christmas shopping,
Gone Christmas shopping,
You should have gone Christmas shopping...

*(Sung to Barnsley fans who were watching their team
go in 5-0 down at half-time during a Carling
Cup tie not that far off Christmas)*

City Is Our Name
(To the tune of Do The Hokey Cokey)

We've got an M an A an N,
a C an I T Y,
We've got the greatest football team,
That money couldn't buy.
We come from Maine Road, Manchester,
And City is our name,
City is our name.

City Is The Team

City is the team,
They're the best team in the land,
Playing the game,
Always in command.
We may lose a point or two,
But never do despair,
'Cos you can't beat the boys in the old light blue,
When they come from Manchester.

CTID
(To the tune of H A P P Y)

City 'til I die,
I'm City 'til I die,
I know I am, I'm sure I am, I'm City 'til I die.

(Popular chant often over in seconds to re-affirm the backing of the faithful during good times and bad)

City Will Win The League (1968)
(To the tune of Halls Of Montezuma To The Shores Of Tripoli)

From the banks of the River Ir-Wy-Ell to the shores of Sicily
We'll fight fight fight for City to win the Football League
We don't care about the other teams
We'll fight fight fight for City to win the Football League
From the banks...

(A chant borne out of the 1968 title triumph that was heard for several years after)

Clichy, Gael I
(To the tune of Pass The Dutchie)

Pass to Clichy on the left-hand side,
Pass to Clichy on the left-hand side,
Give him the ball and he will run, run, run (he is a Blue),
Give him the ball and he will run, run, run (he is a Blue).

*(One of two classic chants based on old songs
for the popular former Arsenal full-back)*

Clichy, Gael II
(To the tune of Dreadlock Holiday)

I don't like Clichy, oh no,
I love him, oh yeah,
I don't like Clichy, oh no,
I love him!

Cole, Andy I

Oh Andy Cole, he's not Man U anymore,
He's not Man U anymore,
Oh Andy Cole,
Oh Andy Cole, he's not Man U anymore.

(Much-travelled former United striker enjoyed one good season with City before moving on, but he proved to be more popular than many people believed he would be thanks largely to a decent scoring ratio)

Cole, Andy II
(To the tune of Let It Snow)

Oh the team we're playing is frightful,
But the Blues are so delightful,
And someone's just scored a goal,
It's Andy Cole, Andy Cole, Andy Cole!

Come In A Taxi
(To the tune of Guantanamera)

Come in a taxi,
You must have come in a taxi,
Come in a taxi,
You must have come in a taxi!

*(Usually sung to teams with very poor away followings such as
Wimbledon in the 1980s and Fulham in more recent years)*

Curle, Keith

Ooh, Curly-Wurly,
Ooh, Curly-Wurly!

*(Basic but popular song for one-time
record signing Keith Curle)*

“ Our version of Blue Moon is sort of Public Image Limited-influenced. At first we thought it was way too psychedelic…it was a tricky one. We were happy to do it and all we need to do now is write a soundtrack for a David Lynch movie. He's not a City fan is he by any chance? ”

– Andy Williams, Doves

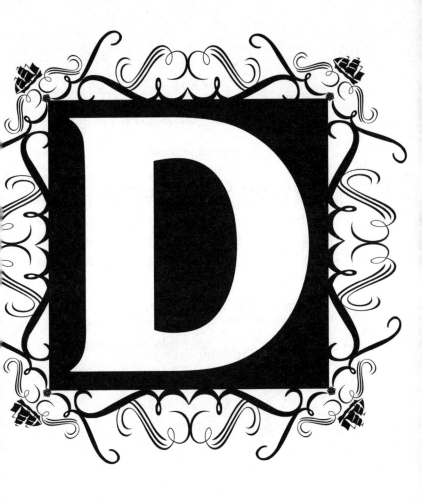

Davis, Wyn
(To the tune of The Mighty Quinn)

Come on without,

Come on within,

You'll not see nothing like the mighty Wyn!

De Bruyne, Kevin
(To the tune of Seven Nation Army by the White Stripes)

Oh, Kevin De Bruyne!

Oh, Kevin de Bruyne!

Oh, Kevin De Bruyne!

Oh, Kevin de Bruyne!

(Repeat)

De Jong Goes Sliding In
(To the tune of When The Saints Go Marching In)

Oh when De Jong (oh when De Jong),
Goes sliding in (goes sliding in),
Oh when De Jong goes sliding in,
There's only going to be one winner,
When De Jong goes sliding in!

*(Popular chant for a popular player, the words have resonance
in regards to the Holland midfielder's uncompromising
tackling style)*

De Jong, Nigel II

De Jong, De Jong, De Jong, De Jong, De Jong!
De Jong, De Jong, De Jong, De Jong, De Jong!
De Jong, De Jong, De Jong, De Jong, De Jong!

(War chant style backing of Dutch enforcer Nigel de Jong)

Dickov, Paul
(To the tune of Guantanamera)

One Paul Dickov,
There's only one Paul Dickov,
One Paul Dickov,
There's only one Paul Dickov,
One Paul Dickov, there's only one Paul Dickov!

Doyle, Mike
(To the tune of Who Do We Appreciate?)

M-I,
M-I-C,
M-I-C-K,
Mick Doyle!

(Popular chant for former skipper and hard man Mike Doyle)

Dunne, Richard
(To the tune of Denis by Blondie)

Dunney, Dunney, he'll put a crush on you,
Dunney, Dunney, he's over six-foot two,
Dunney, Dunney, he's coming after you-oooo.
And when he ran, was like a Chieftain tank,
And when he jumped, the ground beneath him sank.
Dunney, Dunney, he's coming after you-oooo.
Oh Dunney, Dunney's Blue, he's coming after you,
Dunney, Dunney's Blue, he's over six-foot two,
Dunney, Dunney's Blue, he'll put a crush on
you-oooooooo.

*(Brilliant adaptation of Blondie's worldwide smash in
honour of City skipper Richard Dunne)*

Dzeko, Edin I

Woah, oh-oh,
Edin Dzeko, oh-oh!
Edin Dzeko, oh-oh!
(Repeat until bored)

(A difficult tune to describe! Edin Dzeko's chant was often heard echoing around the Etihad Stadium on a matchday)

Dzeko, Edin II
(To the tune of Dynamite)

I throw my hands up in the air sometimes,
Singing Dzeko, Edin Dzeko!

*(Alternative Dzeko song to the tune of
Taio Cruz's worldwide hit)*

Elano I

Jingle bells, jingle bells,
Elano's gonna score,
Oh what fun it is to see Robinho get two more...

*(An affectionate tribute to the Brazilian midfielder who proved so
popular with City fans during his two years with the Blues)*

Elano II
(To the tune of The Music Man)

Ela-Ela-Elano, Elano, Elano,
Ela-Ela-Elano, Ela-Elano!

Elano III

(To the tune of That's Amore!)

When the ball hits the net it's a pretty safe bet – it's Elano.
Left foot or right, the boy's dynamite – it's Elano.
The boy's from Brazil with a bag full of tricks – he's Elano...
When the ball hits the net it's a pretty safe bet – it's Elano!

*(First heard after Elano scored a stunning free-kick
against Newcastle United at the Etihad Stadium)*

England's No.1

England's, Number One!
England, England's Number One,

*(Sung to a succession of City keepers, most notably Joe Corrigan,
Tony Coton and Joe Hart)*

Eriksson, Sven-Goran I
(To the tune of La Donna E Mobile from Verdi's Rigoletto)

> Sven-Goran Eriksson,
> Sven-Goran Eriksson,
> Sven-Goran Eriksson,
> Sven-Goran Eriksson!

Eriksson, Sven-Goran II
(To the tune of The Wall)

We don't need no Phil Scolari,
We don't need Mourinho,
Hey! Thaksin! Leave our Sven alone!

*(When rumours surfaced chairman Thaksin Shinawatra was
thinking of replacing popular City boss Sven-Goran Eriksson
towards the end of the 2007/08 season, City fans came up
with this clever take on Pink Floyd's classic)*

Every Little Thing
(To the tune of Three Little Birds)

City don't worry,
About a thing,
'Cause every little thing,
Is gonna be alright.
City don't worry,
About a thing,
'Cause every little thing,
Is gonna be alright.

(A creation of the supporters group Blue Alliance, the Bob Marley classic Three Little Birds became a popular song in the latter half of the 2010/11 campaign. Tuneful, happy and positive, it can last for a few minutes and is sung whether City are winning, losing or drawing)

❝ I really can't remember when I first heard the song *'Feed The Goat'* but I loved it. I recall the lads coming in at half-time and saying 'did you hear that song, Goat? They're singing about you,' and it just caught on. Some people reckon it was during the 4-0 win over Fulham, others in the away win at Forest – I don't know who thought it up, but I definitely owe them one. The fans would sing it when I scored and if I didn't find the net, I'd put in a few strong challenges and they'd start up again – I wanted to keep that song going! ❞

– Shaun Goater

Feed The Goat

(To the tune of Bread Of Heaven)

Feed the Goat, feed the Goat,
Feed the Goat and he will score!
Feed the Goat and he will score!

*(One of the most popular chants of the past 50 years,
'Feed The Goat' was the serenading fans' anthem for
terrace idol Shaun Goater. With a tune taken from a
Welsh hymn, Goater, considered a journeyman striker
when he joined City from Bristol City in 1998, gradually
won over the supporters to the point he was revered
as a playing club legend. His numerous goals won him
wider recognition as a goal poacher par excellence
and the dignity and humility of such a great goalscorer
further endeared him to the Blues' fans and spawned
'Who Let The Goat Out?' and 'All I Need Is The Air
That I Breathe (and Shaun Goater)'. 'Feed The Goat'
appeared around 1999 and became a song popular
throughout football. Still sung today and saved for
special occasions, Goater and 'Feed The Goat' are
interwoven into the club's fabric and popular culture)*

Fernandinho

La, la, la, la, la, la, la, la – la!
Fern-an-diniho!
La, la, la, la, la, la, la, la – la!
Fern-an-diniho!

(Unknown tune but popular matchday chant)

Fields Of Manchester
(To the tune of Fields Of Athenry)

Low lie the fields of Manchester,
Where once I watched the small Kinky play,
Colin Bell and Francis Lee,
Not forgetting Summerbee,
Oh there's no red in Manchester!

*(Not often heard of late but one of the few songs that links players past
with one from the more recent past)*

Fight 'Til The End
(To the tune of Sloop John B)

We'll fight 'til the end,
We'll fight 'til the end,
We're Man City,
We'll fight 'til the end!

*(A song borne out of City's refusal to give up
on the 2011/12 title race despite falling eight points
behind United with just six games to go)*

Fowler, Robbie
(To the tune of Yellow Submarine)

We all live in a Robbie Fowler house,
Robbie Fowler house,
Robbie Fowler house.
We all live in a Robbie Fowler house,
Robbie Fowler house,
Robbie Fowler house.
No.1 is Robbie's house,
No.2 is Robbie's house,
No.3 is Robbie's house,
No.4 is Robbie's house,
No.5 is Robbie's house.
We all live in a Robbie Fowler house,
Robbie Fowler house,
Robbie Fowler house.

*(Sung after revelations that Robbie owned more
than 80 houses in the North West)*

Given, Shay
(To the tune of Volare)

He comes from Donegal,
He never drops the ball,
He's called Shaymus,
He's the famous,
City Wonderwall...

Goater, Shaun I
(To the tune of The Air That I Breathe)

Sometimes,
All I need is the air that I breathe,
And Shaun Goater.

Goater, Shaun II
(To the tune of Who Let The Dogs Out?)

Who let the Goat out?
Who, who, who-who?
Who let the Goat out?
Who, who, who-who?
Who let the Goat out?
Who, who, who-who?
Who let the Goat out?
Who, who, who-who?

(This song had rumbled on for a few weeks but was sung by every City fan as the players left the pitch following the last Maine Road Manchester derby. City had won 3-1, Goater had scored twice and the goals were his 99th and 100th for the Blues)

Goater, Shaun III

Remember, remember the ninth of November,
The last Maine Road derby will last forever,
The score was level, the Goat fed by Neville,
Silly boy should have known for sure,
Feed the Goat and he will score.

Goater, Shaun IV
(To the tune of Jesus Christ Superstar)

Shaun Goater, superstar
How many goals has he scored so far?
One or two, or maybe three
But he scored with his gut and we're at
Wem-ber-lee.

*(This song pays tribute to cult hero Shaun Goater and his
ability to score goals with every part of his anatomy –
including one that brushed off his upper body in the play-off
semi-final against Wigan to set up the 1999 third tier final
with Gillingham)*

Goater, Shaun V
(To the tune of Come On Feel The Noize)

So come on feed the Goat,
Come on feed the Goat,
He wants goals, goals, goals!
He wants goals, goals, goals!
So come on feed the Goat,
Come on the feed the Goat,
He scores goals, goals, goals!
He scores goals, goals, goals!

*(Yet another Goater classic and arguably he has more catchy
songs than any other City player – this was heard emanating
from the North Stand after he'd scored during
a 4-1 win over Fulham)*

God Bless City
(To the tune of Only Fools And Horses)

Some championships, no Champions League,
Some FA Cup, No LDV,
We don't care, lose or draw,
You'll always hear the City roar,
God Bless Man City,
Viiiiiva Man City,
God bless Man City,
C'est Magnifique, Man City!
A proper club, Man City,
Pride of the north, Man City!
Man City!

(Improvised chant and not heard often but great lyrics!)

Gonna Get Along Without You Now

You told everybody that we were friends,
This is where the friendship ends,
Aha, wo-oh, gonna get along without you now!
Aha, wo-oh, gonna get along without you now!

*(Intelligent dig at the media and other football fans who used to call City
their second club and retain affection for the Blues' rollercoaster existence
– until we started to win trophies)*

Greatest Of Them All

Some speak of Man United and Bolton as well,
Of Oldham and Bury,
I've also heard tell.
But the team to remember,
The team to recall,
Is Manchester City, the greatest of them all...
But the team to remember,
The team to recall,
Is Manchester City, the greatest of them all...

Guardiola, Pep
(To the tune of Glad All Over)

And we've got – Guardiola!
We've got – Guardiola!
We've got – Guardiola!
Say you're mine-i-i-i-i-ine!

(First song for Pep sung on matchday 1 at the Etihad!)

Haaland, Alfie
(To the tune of London Bridge)

Alfie Haaland is a Blue,
Is a Blue, is a Blue,
Alfie Haaland is a Blue,
He hates Man U.

Hareide, Aage
(To the tune of We Are The Champions)

Oggy Hareide!
Oggy Hareide!

Hart, Joe
(To the tune of Ossie's Dream)

Joe Hart do the Poznan,
Joe Hart do the Poznan,
Na na na nah,
Na nan a nah.
Joe Hart do the Poznan,
Joe Hart do the Poznan,
Na na na nah,
Na nan a nah.

(Sung – usually by the South Stand – until Hart responds)

Hartford, Asa
(To the tune of Roly Poly)

Oh Asa Hartford, Asa Hartford,
Na, na, na, na, na hey,
Oh Asa Hartford, Asa Hartford,
Na, na, na, na, na hey!

Horlock, Kevin
(To the tune of Bobby Shafto)

Su-per, super Kev,
Su-per, super Kev,
Su-per, super Kev,
Su-per Kevin Horlock!

Huckerby, Darren

He can tackle,
He can jump,
He can run like Forrest Gump,
Huckerby, Huckerby!

Hulk

You're not incredible,
You're not incredible,
You're not incredible,
You're not incredible!

*(Off-the-cuff chant sung during a match against
Porto when Brazilian striker Hulk had something of
an off-night against the Blues. He didn't turn green
but it brought a smile to the faces of the majority
in the home crowd)*

I Got Sunshine
(To the tune of My Girl)

I got sunshine on a cloudy day,
When it's cold outside,
I got the month of May.
I guess you say,
What can make me feel this way?
Cityyyyy!
Talking 'bout City, City!

(Pleasant, dreamy tribute to the Blues)

Iheanacho, Kelechi I
(To the tune of Freed From Desire)

Kelechi's on fire,
Your defence is terrified,
Kelechi's on fire,
Your defence is terrified!
Na, na, na, na, na, na etc

(City fans' brief attempt at the 'Will Grigg' classic)

Iheanacho, Kelechi II

Iheanach-io! Iheanach-io!
Iheanach-io,
Iheanach-io!

*(One of a growing number of Kelechi serenades – first sung after
his hat-trick away to Aston Villa in 2015)*

In 1963...

In 1963 when we fell to Division Two,
The Stretford End cried out aloud,
'It's the end for you Sky Blue'.
Joe Mercer came,
We played the game,
We went to Rotherham,
And won 1-0,
And we were back into Division One.
We've won the league, we've won the League Cup,
We've been to Europe, too.
And when we win the league again,
We'll sing this song to you,
City, City, City, City, City!

*(Popular and long-lasting song that is still often heard – a real
passed down chant – from father to son or daughter)*

Ireland, Stephen

Ireland is Superman,
Ireland is Superman,
Ireland is Superman,
Ireland is Superman!

(When Stephen Ireland suddenly found confidence in his own abilities, he became the most important player in the City side for 18 months before his form began to wane. With the chant well-established, after scoring one particular goal, Ireland dropped his shorts to reveal a pair of Superman trunks!)

Ireland's Granny
(To the tune of Molly Malone)

Alive, alive oh,
Alive, alive oh,
Stephen Ireland's two grannies,
Alive, alive oh!

(Inventive chant which was first heard after it was revealed Ireland had left the Republic of Ireland squad after telling officials his grandmother had passed away. It was later revealed it was a ploy to return home and both his grans, thankfully, were alive and well)

Istanbul

Istanbul, Istanbul we are coming,
Istanbul, Istanbul I pray,
Istanbul, Istanbul we are coming,
We are coming at the end of May.

*(Song that was sung during City's 2009/10 Europa League run
which was ended by Hamburg at the quarter-final stage – another
version along the same lines was chanted in 2010/11 with Dublin
replacing Istanbul)*

Jingle Bells

Jingle bells,
Jingle bells,
Jingle all the way,
Oh what fun it is to see,
City win away!
[Repeat]

(Festive song usually only heard when the Blues have a two-goal cushion on the road – anything sooner would be tempting fate!)

Joe Mercer's Aces
(To the tune of Blaydon Races)

Oh, me lads,
You should have seen them coming,
Fastest team in the land,
Should have seen them running,
All the lads and lasses, all with smiling faces,
Walking down to Maine Road,
To see Joe Mercer's aces!

(Popular football chant adapted by each set of supporters who sing it and undoubtedly originating from Newcastle United fans)

Just Like Watching Brazil
(To the tune of Blue Moon)

Brazil,

It's just like watching Brazil,

It's just like watching Brazil,

It's just like watching Brazil.

(No definitive date when first sang, but certainly first heard by a national TV audience when a Georgi Kinkladze-inspired City dismantled Oxford United 4-1 in 1996/97. Barnsley later adopted the song as their own and won widespread praise for the song – but it began with City!)

Karma, Karma, Karma C'mon City!
(To the tune of Karma Chameleon)

Karma karma karma karma karma come on City,
We're going up,
We're going up!

(The Culture Club classic was at its loudest during City's numerous promotion attempts during the 'yo-yo years')

Keegan Wonderland
(To the tune of Walking In A Winter Wonderland)

There's only one, Kevin Keegan,
One Kevin Keegan,
We're walking along, singing this song,
Walking in a Keegan wonderland!

(The 'Messiah' had just one song during his four years as City boss – this one!)

Keep The Blue Flag Flying High
(To the tune of Oh Christmas Tree)

Hello, hello, how do you do?
We are the boys in laser blue,
Wherever we go, we'll fear no foe,
'Cause the blue flag's flying high,
Up flying high, up in the sky,
We'll keep the blue flag flying high,
From Manchester to the Bernabeu,
We'll keep the blue flag flying high!

Kidd, Brian

Kiddo, Kiddo, Kiddo!

Kippax

We are the Kippax!
We are the Kippax!

*(Still sung a decade after leaving Maine Road,
usually by the South Standers)*

Kompany, Vincent I
(To the tune of Go West)

Vincent, Vincent Kompany,
Vincent, Vincent Kompany,
Vincent, Vincent Kompany,
Vincent, Vincent Kompany!

(Anthemic and uplifting song for the City skipper)

Kompany, Vincent II
(To the tune of The Addams Family)

He's big, he's tall, he's scary,
His head's not very hairy,
He makes defenders wary,
It's Vincent Kompany!

*(An affectionate chant, first heard at Sunderland during the
2009/10 campaign, for City's Belgian skipper)*

Kompany, Vincent III
(To the tune of Simon & Garfunkel's Mrs Robinson)

And here's to you,
Vincent Kompany,
City loves you more than you will know, woah,
woah, woah!
God bless you please,
Vincent Kompany,
City loves you more than you will know, woah,
woah, woah!

(Very popular chant for the skipper)

Kompany, Vincent IV
(To the tune of Bear Necessities)

Cause we've got Vincent Kompany
The Rock at the back for Man City
Don't worry about Zlatan or Rooney....

'Cause we've got Vincent Kompany
He's more than you will ever need
Don't worry about clean sheets or trophies...

'Cause we've got Vincent Kompany
The rock at the back for Man City
Don't worry about Mahrez or Vardy

'Cause we've got Vincent Kompany
He's more than you will ever need
He's the captain and leader of Man City!

Kompany, Vincent V
(To the tune of Lily the Pink)

We'll drink, a drink, a drink, to Vinny the king, the
king, the king.
He's the leader of Man City.
He's the greatest, central defender that the
worrrrrld, has ever seen.

Kompany, Vincent VI
(To the tune of Let It Be)

Kom-pa-ny, Kom-pa-ny, Kom-pa-ny, Kom-pa-ny
Speaking words of wisdom,
Kom-pa-ny.

Lee, Francis

(To the tune of My Mammy)

Franny, Franny,
He'd walk a million miles,
To kick Nobby Stiles,
Oh, Franny!

Leeds United

You're worse than Leeds United!
You're worse than Leeds United!

*(After an ultra-defensive Leeds United played City at Maine
Road, this chant was born. The Lilywhites had drawn 0-0
perhaps half-a-dozen times during the 1981/82 campaign
but left City with a 1-0 defeat courtesy of a last-gasp Kevin
Reeves winner. Any team who bored the Kippax thereafter
was treated to this song and, in particular, for the next visit
of Leeds United, the City fans informed them that they
were, in fact, worse than themselves!)*

Lescott, Joleon I
(To the tune of Sloop John B)

He's top of the league,
He's top of the le-ee-eague,
Joleon Lescott, he's top of the league.

(Sang in response to any insulting songs aimed at Joleon)

Lescott, Joleon II
(To the tune of Ossie's Dream)

Lescott's going to Europe,
Lescott's going to Europe,
Na na na na,
Na na na na!

*(First heard away to Everton when the Goodison Park
faithful were firing pelters at the England defender)*

Macclesfield

Are you watching?
Are you watching?
Are you watching Macclesfield?
Are you watching Macclesfield?

(City fans won universal praise as the Blues slipped into the third tier of English football for the third time, despite leading 5-2 at Stoke City)

Maine Road

Maine Road, Maine Road what a wonderful place.
In organisation we set the pace.
We've forward and half-backs and full-backs, too,
All proud to be wearing maroon and sky blue!

Man City
(To the tune of Ant Music)

So come on down to Maine Road,

And do yourself a favour...

Your football's lost its taste,

So try another flavour...

Man City oi oi oi oi!

Man City oi oi oi oi!

*(Classic adaptation of a huge 1980s hit by
Adam and the Ants and popular for a short time)*

Manchester!
(To the tune of The Banana Splits)

Manchester, la, la, la!
Manchester, la, la, la!

Manchester Boy

We go down to Maine Road, we go for a ride,
We go to watch City, the pride of Moss Side,
We cheer on the Sky Blues, we cheer on our team,
We know that we can't lose, so we let off steam,
We go to away games, it's worth all the fare,
The guard pulls and wrecked trains, we just do not care,
At Maine Road it's different, we treat it with care,
We never throw litter, we don't even swear,
Because it's my City, it's my pride and my joy,
And I'm just so glad I'm a Manchester boy.

Manchester City FC
(To the tune of The Wild Rover)

And it's Manchester City,
Manchester City FC,
We're by far the greatest team,
The world has ever seen!

*(An old, timeless favourite that has been sung for
several decades)*

Mancini, Roberto
(To the tune of Volare)

Mancini, who-oh-oh-ah,
Mancini, who-oh-oh-ah,
He came from Italy, to manage Man City.
Mancini, who-oh-oh-ah,
Mancini, who-oh-oh-ah,
He came from Italy, to manage Man City.

*(Sung shortly after Mancini first arrived but delivered with
much more gusto as he guided City to greater things as the
months went by)*

MANCINI, ROBERTO

Mancini, who-oh-oh-ah,
Mancini, who-oh-oh-ah,
He came from Italy,
Has pasta for his tea,
Mancini, who-oh-oh-ah,
Mancini, who-oh-oh-ah!

(Slight variation on the previous song – a more fun version)

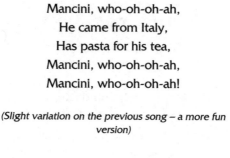

Marching In
(To the tune of When The Saints Go Marching In)

Oh when the Blues, go marching in,
Oh when the Blues go marching in,
I want to be in that number,
Oh when the Blues go marching in...

Marsh, Rodney
(To the tune of Son Of My Father)

Oh, Rodney, Rodney,
Rodney, Rodney, Rodney, Rodney,
Rodney Marsh.

*(Iconic chant sung during Marsh's mid-seventies heyday.
Simple, classy and befitting of his mercurial talent)*

MCFC OK!

MC,
MCF,
MCFC,
OK!

MCFC II
(To the tune of Son Of My Father)

Oh Man City,
The only football team to come from Manchester!

Mercer, Joe
(To the tune of Grocer Jack)

Joe Mercer, Joe Mercer,
Is it true what people say?
We're gonna win...the Football League?

Merrily We Roll Along
(To the tune of London Bridge Is Falling Down)

Merrily we roll along,
Roll along, roll along,
Merrily we roll along,
Up the Football League.

*(As the lyrics indicate, a gentle song from yesteryear
that has been condemned to history)*

Morrison, Andy
(To the tune of Son Of My Father)

Oh, Andy, Andy,
Andy, Andy, Andy, Andy Morrison!

Nasri, Samir I
(To the tune of Give It Up)

Na, na, na, na, na, na, na, na, na, na, na
Samir Nas-er-i, Nas-er-i,
Samir Nasri!

Nasri, Samir II
(To the tune of Ruby)

Sammy, Sammy, Sammy, Sammy!
Na-as-eri!
Sammy, Sammy, Sammy, Sammy!
Na-as-eri!

*(Thought up by none other than Micah Richards and aired on City's
website during an episode of Inside City)*

Negredo, Alvaro

Feed the Beast,
Feed the Beast,
Feed the Beast and he will score!
Feed the Beast and he will score!

*(Improvised Feed The Goat chant for
Alvaro 'The Beast' Negredo)*

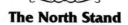

The North Stand

Bertie Mee said to Don Revie,
Have you heard of the North Bank Highbury?
Don said no, I don't think so,
But I've heard of the North Stand, Maine Road.

““ I love the song 'Oh When De Jong goes sliding in'! It's always great to have the appreciation of fans because it shows that you're working hard and doing well. When we get to Wembley in a final, I might give the fans a verse of it myself! ””

– Nigel De Jong

Oh What a Night

Oh what a night,
One second half in two thousand and four,
Three nil down and Joey shown the door,
I remember what a night!

Oh what a night
Shaun Wright-Phillips showed you how it's done,
Distin, Bosvelt joined in on the fun,
I remember what a night!

Oh what a night,
Two minutes left before some extra time,
Macken shows up on the six-yard line,
4-3 up oh what a night!

*(First heard shortly after City's remarkable FA Cup 4th round replay
away to Tottenham during which 10-man City went in 3-0 down at
half-time only to win 4-3 on a dramatic night at White Hart Lane)*

On Our Way

We're on our way,
We're on our way, we're on our way,
we're on our way,
How we got here I don't know,
Will we stay there? I don't care,
All I know is City's on their way.

*(First heard during the latter stages of the Blues' promotion
push in 1999/2000 and sung with added gusto at the
promotion party that was Ewood Park 2000 following City's
4-1 win over Blackburn)*

Once A Blue...
(To the tune of Tom Hark)

Once a Blue,
Always a Blue,
Once a Blue,
Always a Blue,
Once a Blue,
Always a Blue.

(Sung on several occasions for different reasons – once it was for Wayne Rooney who had famously claimed the words of the song in connection with his Everton roots – before he signed for United. Other times it's been aimed at returning City players in the colours of other teams)

One City
(To the tune of Blue Moon)

City!
There's only one City!
There's only one City!
There's only one City!

(Often sung to clubs who also have City in their name)

One, Two, Three...
(To the tune of Once I Caught A Fish Alive)

One, two, three, four, five,
We are City we will strive.
Six, seven, eight, nine, ten,
We are going to win again.
Who scored, was it Jo?
Elano or Robinho?
Defence, midfield, we will fight,
With Shaun Wright-Phillips on the right.

Onuoha, Nedum
(To the tune of We Are The Champions!)

Nedum Onuoha!
Nedum Onuoha!
Nedum Onuoha!
Nedum Onuoha!

*(A simple chant sung for City's former Academy
graduate over a period of several years)*

Pardoe, Glyn I
(To the tune of Heigh-ho)

Pardoe, Pardoe,

We're off to Mexico,

With Bell and Lee and Summerbee,

Pardoe, Pardoe, Pardoe, Pardoe...

*(Sung in 1970 as City fans voiced their expectation that unsung
hero Glyn Pardoe would earn an England call-up
for the Mexico '70 World Cup)*

Pardoe, Glyn II
(To the tune of The Mighty Quinn)

Come on without,

Come on within,

You ain't seen nothing like the mighty Glyn!

Pearce, Stuart I

Psycho!
Psycho!
Psycho!

*(Inherited from his Nottingham Forest days where
he genuinely was Psycho in residence!)*

Pearce, Stuart II
(To the tune of Give Peace A Chance)

All we are saying,
Is give Pearce a chance,
All we are saying,
Is give Pearce a chance.

*(Classic re-working of the John Lennon classic as Stuart
Pearce stepped into the breach as caretaker manager
following Kevin Keegan's resignation)*

Pellegrini, Manuel

Sheikh Mansour,
Went to Spain
In a Lamborghini
And brought us back a manager
Manuel Pellegrini!

(An ode to former boss Manuel Pellegrini)

Phelan, Terry
(To the tune of You've Lost That Loving Feeling)

We've got that Terry Phelan,
Oh that Terry Phelan,
We've got that Terry Phelan,
And he's fast, fast, fast, woah-woah-woah.

(One of the best adaptations of a popular song, it was sung in honour of the rapid Irish international Terry Phelan during his time at City)

The Poznan
(To the tune of Let's All Do The Conga)

Let's all do the Poznan,
Let's all do the Poznan,
Na, na, na, na!
Na, na, na, na!
Let's all do the Poznan,
Let's all do the Poznan,
Na, na, na, na!
Na, na, na, na!

*(The song that generally precedes a Poznan dance – often
just to liven things up and usually rounded off with
a hearty version of 'City! City! City!')*

Pride Of Manchester
(To the tune of Bread Of Heaven)

We're the pride,
We're the pride,
We're the pride of Manchester,
We're the pride of Manchester!

*(Sung whether City are midway down the third tier of
English football or on top of the Premier League)*

Que Sera, Sera

Que sera, sera,
Whatever will be, will be,
We're going to Wem-ber-ley,
Que sera, sera.

Que sera, sera,
Whatever will be, will be,
We're going to win the league,
Que sera, sera!

*(An old football chant and sung by many clubs who are in with
a chance of a trip to Wembley. It used to be sung with scarves
waved around in circles at head height)*

Niall Quinn's Disco Pants

Niall Quinn's disco pants are the best,
They go up from his ass to his chest...
They are better than Adam and the Ants,
Niall Quinn's disco pants!

*(Though later adopted by Sunderland fans, this song
was originally created by City fans during a night out
on a pre-season tour in Penola, Italy, in 1992. There
had allegedly been a bust-up with City team-mate
Steve McMahon and Quinn had removed his torn
and bloodied shirt and was dancing with Rick Holden
wearing just a pair of cut-off jeans. He was unaware
that there were a group of hardcore City fans
watching and they treated him to what Quinn later
described as "the first performance of the song that
will follow me until the end of my career!")*

Quinn, Niall II
(To the tune of Ole, Ole, Ole!)

Ole, ole, ole, ole,
Niall Quinn, Niall Quinn!

Quinn, Niall III
(To the tune of The Mighty Quinn)

Come on without,
Come on within,
You've not seen nothing like the Mighty Quinn.

Remember When?
(To the tune of Remember Then)

Re-mem-mem, re-member-member,
Re-mem-mem, remember-member
Re-mem-mem, remember, member
– when – when,
City scored ten?

*(This song refers to City's mammoth 10-1 win
over Huddersfield Town in 1987)*

Richards, Micah
(To the tune of Hey, Mickey!)

Hey Micah, you're so fine,
You scored a goal in injury-time,
Hey Micah! Hey Micah!

*(A certain situation or goal can spark a song – as in this case
with Micah Richards' injury-time equaliser at Aston Villa in 2007
spawning a version of Toni Basil's 1980s hit 'Hey, Mickey!'
Wasn't around for too long but still fondly remembered)*

Robinho I

We've got Robinho, we've got Robinho,
We've got Robinho, we've got Robinho.

*(This song was famously first aired to a live audience of
millions at midnight on transfer deadline day 2008 as Sky
Sports News announced, live from the Etihad Stadium, that
the Brazilian star had joined the Blues from Real Madrid
just seconds before the window shut)*

Robinho II
(To the tune of Amarillo)

Show us the way to score Robinho,
You can even skin Evra and Rio,
Passing balls to Shauny and Castillo,
Oh our Robinho loves City.

Na na na na na na na nah, City!
Na na na na na na na nah, City!
Na na na na na na na nah,
Our Robinho loves City!

Robinho III
(To the tune of That's Not My Name by Ting-Tings)

They call him skilful,
They call him great,
Manchester City,
We sing his name,
Robinho,
Robinho,
Robinho,
Robinho.

Robinho IV
(To the tune of Heigh-ho)

Heigh-ho, heigh-ho,
We've got Robinho,
With Petrov, Jo and Elano,
Heigh-ho, heigh-ho, heigh-ho, heigh-ho.

Robinho V
(To the tune of Volare)

Robinho whoah-oh, Robinho whoah-oh,
He came on deadline day!
He'll probably score today!
Robinho whoah-oh, Robinho whoah-oh!

*(Robinho – in regards to chants and songs,
he's the player who just kept giving!)*

Robinho VI
(To the tune of Wheels On The Bus)

Robinho on the bus goes round and round,
Round and round, round and round,
Robinho on the bus goes round and round,
All day long.

*(When a newspaper reported Robinho was getting around
Manchester by taking the occasional bus trip, the City fans
loved the rumour and came up with this mini classic. He
later denies he'd been on the 42X to Didsbury – or any
other Manchester bus for that matter
– but the legend lives on!)*

Robinho VII
(To the tune of Oh Christmas Tree)

Robinho, Robinho,
You make Ronaldo look pretty slow.
Robinho, Robinho,
You're our Brazilian dynamo.
So when we win the Premier League,
And when we win the Champions League,
There's only one song that we'll sing,
Robinho's our Brazilian king.

*(First heard when City travelled to play
Schalke in the Europa League)*

Ronaldinho
(To the tune of London Bridge Is Falling Down)

Ronaldinho is a Blue,
Is a Blue, is a Blue,
Ronaldinho is a Blue,
He hates Man U!

*(Sung in honour of Brazilian superstar Ronaldinho during
a friendly with Barcelona to open the Etihad Stadium.
Ronaldinho – who had just turned down a move to United
– left the pitch to a standing ovation and looked a little
bemused by it all)*

Rosler, Uwe
(To the tune of Go West)

Uwe, Uwe Ros-e-ler,
Uwe, Uwe Ros-e-ler,
Uwe, Uwe Ros-e-ler,
Uwe, Uwe Ros-e-ler!

*(Very popular song during the mid-to-late 1990s
in honour of German cult hero Uwe Rosler*

Samaras, Georgios

Feed the Greek, feed the Greek,
Feed the Greek and he will score,
Feed the Greek and he will score!

*(Georgios Samaras' time with City barely merited such an
iconic chant, but such was the talent famine and lack of
goals during Stuart Pearce's reign as City boss, he was
treated to his own version of 'Feed The Goat')*

Sane, Leroy

Sane and Sterling are the kings,
They are the ki-ings,
Of the wings!

(Unknown tune)

Santa Cruz, Roque

(To the tune of Santa Claus Is Coming To Town)

Oh! You better watch out,
You better not cry,
You better not shout,
I'm telling you why,
Santa Cruz is coming to town!

Better watch out!
Better beware!
He's good on the floor,
He's good in the air,
Santa Cruz is coming to town!

He's kicking the ball,
His shots are quite nice,
You never know if he'll score just once or twice,
Santa Cruz is coming to town.

*(Sadly, this song is the most memorable part of
Roque Santa Cruz's time with City!)*

Score When We Want

(To the tune of Sloop John B)

We'll score when we want,
We'll score when we wa-aa-aa-nt
We're Man City, we'll score when we want!

*(A City version of United's 'We'll Do What We Want', the
song was first heard during the 2011/12 season when City's
forwards were breaking all club scoring records)*

Shall We Show You What To Do?

(To the tune of Bread Of Heaven)

Shall we show you?
Shall we show you?
Shall we show you what to do?
Shall we show you what to do?

*(When away fans celebrate goals with a mocking Poznan,
the City fans usually respond by doing a far
more polished demonstration)*

Silva, David I
(To the tune of Hi Ho Silver Lining)

And it's, hi ho Silva's lightning,
Every time he plays its frightening,
I see that Blue moon rising,
But I won't make a fuss,
Because it's time for us.

(A tribute to City's brilliant midfield magician, David Silva)

Silva, David II
(To the tune of You Are My Sunshine)

Oh David Silva,
He drinks sangria,
He came to City,
To bring us joy.
He's five-foot seven,
He's football heaven,
So please don't take our Silva away.

(Adapted from Liverpool's classic song for Luis Garcia)

Silva, David III
(To the tune of The Great Escape)

His name is Silva, oh David Silva,
He scored the fifth goal at Old Trafford,
His name is Silva, oh David Silva,
He is the maestro of the Etihad.

*(The words are made to fit in yet another
tribute to City's brilliant Spaniard)*

Silva, David IV
(To the tune of Every Little Thing)

Every little thing he does is magic,
Every little thing he does is class,
And every goal that City score it's certain,
It's from a David Silva pass.

*(A song first heard towards the end of the 2011/12 season
in reverence to the man Shaun Wright-Phillips
famously called 'Merlin')*

Sing When You're Fishing
(To the tune of Guantanamera)

Sing when you're fishing,
You only sing when you're fishing,
Sing when you're fishing,
You only sing when you're fishing!

*(City fans, bored during a dour game at Blundell Park,
playfully taunt the Grimsby Town fans)*

Sons Of MCFC
(To the tune of Sons Of The Sea)

City's the team,
We are the best team in the land,
Playing the game, always in command,
We may lose a point or two, but we never do
despair,
'Cos you can't beat the boys in the old light blue,
When they come from Manchester.

*(A popular terrace chant in the 1940s and 1950s
– and a world away from the harsher songs of today)*

Singing The Blues

I never felt more like singing the Blues,
City win, United lose,
Oh City,
You've got me singing the Blues!

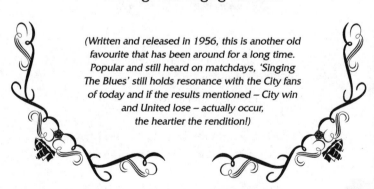

*(Written and released in 1956, this is another old
favourite that has been around for a long time.
Popular and still heard on matchdays, 'Singing
The Blues' still holds resonance with the City fans
of today and if the results mentioned – City win
and United lose – actually occur,
the heartier the rendition!)*

Stand Up!
(To the tune of Go West)

Stand up, if you love City,
Stand up, if you love City,
Stand up, if you love City,
Stand up, if you love City!

Sterling, Raheem

He's top of the league,
He's top of the league,
Raheem Sterling – he's top of the league!

(City fans' response to any opposition supporters who target Sterling during matches)

Summerbee, Mike
(To the tune of Sha La La La Lee)

Sh la la la Summerbee,
Sh la la la Summerbee!
Who the bloomin' heck is he?
The greatest centre forward in history,
United 1 and City 3,
Sha la la la Summerbee,
He came to City from Swindon Town,
Sha la la la Summerbee,
Little did they know he was England bound,
Sha la la la Summerbee.

*(Popular version of the Small Faces' song in the late sixties
for charismatic City and England forward Mike Summerbee
when Buzzer was terrorising defences up and
down the land)*

Super City
(To the tune of Sailing)

We are City,
We are City,
Super City, from Maine Road,
We are City, Super City,
We are City, from Maine Road.

(Based on Rod Stewart's huge hit, several clubs adopted the tune to fit their club and City were no different. Still popular today because of the Maine Road connotations, and because ultimately, it is a great song to sing in a stadium)

❝ Yeah, I'd have a little jam with him. He can't speak English though – I've met him! But I love that he doesn't care and just goes out and does his thing. If he ever wants to bust the guitar out and do a bit, I'm always available! **❞**

– Noel Gallagher on Carlos Tevez

Take Me Home
(To the tune of Country Road)

Take me home to Maine Road,
To the place I belong,
On the Kippax,
To see the City,
Take me home to Maine Road.

(Direct response to Manchester United's song of a similar vein)

Tevez, Carlos I
(To the tune of London Bridge Is Falling Down)

Carlos Tevez is a Blue, is a Blue, is a Blue,
Carlos Tevez is a Blue,
He hates Man U!

(When Carlos Tevez signed for City, this was the first and most immediate song the City fans came up with)

Tevez, Carlos II
(Tune the tune of God Save Ireland)

Who's that man from Argentina?
Who's that man you didn't sign?
He didn't sign for you,
'Cause his heart was set on Blue,
Now Carlos is City's 32!

*(A dig at the fact United failed to take up the option to
sign Tevez – a cult hero with United fans until his defection
across the city)*

Tevez, Carlos III
(To the tune of Sloop John B)

He wants to go home,
He wants to go ho-o-ome,
Carlos Tevez, he wants to go home!

(Following his self-imposed three-month exile in Argentina during the 2011/12 season, opposition fans began to sing the above song, mocking the Argentinian's commitment to City. When he began scoring goals for the Blues again, the City fans began singing it, too, but with more than a little irony)

Tevez, Carlos IV
(To the tune of Don't Cry For Me Argentina)

Don't cry for them Carlos Tevez,
The truth is they can't afford you,
All through the summer, where were you going?
We'll keep our Tevez,
You keep your Owen.

That's Man City!

(To the tune of That's Amore)

When your team it goes down,
And you still fill your ground,
That's amore!

When you go down again,
And you still fill it then,
That's amore!

(City fans have remained loyal during the club's darkest days and this song was hatched as a response to any opposition fans who suggest City's gates were poor before the Blues' more recent successes)

The Only...
(To the tune of Son Of My Father)

Oh, Man City,
The only English team to win the championship.

(A claim by City fans dating back to the late 1960s that no other team has won the league title with 11 Englishmen)

The Only Team In Manchester
(To the tune of The Ants Go Marching)

The only team in Manchester, City! City!
The best supporters in the world, City! City!
With pride in battle on our chest,
We'll fight to prove that we're the best,
Super City, pride of Manchester!
Na, na, na, na, na, na, na, na, na,
Na-nah!
Na, na, na, na, na, na, na, na, na,
Na-nah!
Na, na, na, na, na, na, na, na, na, na, na, na, na, na,
Super City, pride of Manchester!

There's A Hole...
(To the tune of There's A Hole In My Bucket)

There's a hole in the ceiling,
And the cantilever's leaking,
No money coming in...
Chuck the whole lot in the bin.

*(Gentle song about United from the 1950s
– how times have changed!)*

This Is How It Feels

This is how it feels to be City,
This is how it feels to walk tall,
This is how it feels when your club owes
nothing at all,
Nothing at all.

35 years
(To the tune of Tom Hark)

35 years, and we're still here,
35 years, and we're still here,
35 years, and we're still here,
35 years, and we're still here!

*(City fans used a song that mocked the amount of years
since the club had won a trophy as a proud testament of
unswerving loyalty – though that ended with
the FA Cup win in 2011)*

Tiatto, Danny
(To the tune of The Music Man)

There is an Aussie man he plays in our team,
And when we see him play you will hear us sing
(what do we sing?)

Tia-tia, Tiatto, Tiatto, Tiatto,
Tia-tia, Tiatto,
Tia-Tiatto!

*(Sung during the 2001/02 season for tough-tackling
defender Danny Tiatto)*

Toure, Yaya I
(To the tune of Hey Jude by The Beatles)

Ya, Ya, Ya,
Yaya-Ya-Ya,
Yaya-Ya-Ya,
Tou-re!

(Belted out in honour of City's brilliant Ivorian powerhouse Yaya Toure and sung loudly during the Manchester derby of April 2012)

Toure, Yaya II
(To the tune of Camptown Races)

Who put the ball in United's net?
Yaya, Yaya,
Who put the ball in United's net?
Yaya, Yaya Toure!

Toure, Yaya III
(To the tune of Sunday, Bloody Sunday)

I can't believe the news today.
An eight-point lead has gone, they've thrown it
all away,
How long, how long have we waited now?
How long, how long?
Toure!
Yaya, Yaya Toure,
Yaya, Yaya Toure!

*(Some songs can only be sung for a limited time and
this one emerged after City ate United's eight-point
lead away during the 2011/12 title race run-in)*

Toure, Yaya IV
(To the tune of Knowing Me, Knowing You)

Knowing me, knowing you – Yaya,
We're gonna make you a Blue,
Knowing me, knowing you – Yaya,
We are gonna sign him this time, it's true,
Knowing me, knowing you, we will make him a
Blue.

Trick Or Treating
(To the tune of Guantanamera)

Gone trick or treating,
You should have gone trick or treating,
Gone trick or treating,
You should have gone trick or treating!

*(A song saved for when City are winning on Hallowe'en
night – it needs a particular set of circumstances and has
only been heard once or twice as a result!)*

Tueart, Dennis

Dennis Tueart, king of all Geordies!

66 I confess one thing, I'm glad to hear City fans at the stadium chant my name to the tune of 'Volare'. 99

– Roberto Mancini

Varadi, Imre

Imre, Imre Varadi,
Imre Varadi,
Imre Var-ah-ah-di – hey!'

(Russian Cossack theme for the cult late 1980s striker)

Vieria, Patrick I
(To the tune of Sloop John B)

He's won it five times,
He's won it five ti-i-imes,
Patrick Vieira, he's won it five times!

*(This was Patrick Vieira's first City song and was heard,
fittingly, as he walked around the pitch at Wembley having
won the FA Cup for, as the song suggests,
a record fifth time)*

Vieira, Patrick II
(To the tune of Volare)

Vieira, whoah-woah!
Vieira, whoah-oh-oh,
He came from Italy,
To play for Man City!

Vonk, Michel

Ooh, Vonky, Vonky,
Ooh, Vonky, Vonky!

Wanchope, Paulo
(To the tune of Top Cat)

Wanchope, the unbelievable Wanchope,
The irresistible, close friends get to call him Paulo,
Give him the ball and he will score you a goal,
Wanchope, the unbelievable, leader of our line,
He is top, he is hip, he is championship,
He's the one tip top, Wanchope!

*(Terrific take on cartoon Top Cat theme for
Costa Rican striker Paulo Wanchope)*

We All Follow...
(To the tune of Land Of Hope And Glory)

We all follow the City,
Over land and sea, and Stretford!
We all follow the City on to victory!

We Are The Kippax
(To the tune of The Mighty Quinn)

On top of all England,
Now stand the Sky Blues,
Who we will follow,
Win or lose.
'Cos we are the Kippax,
And when we cheer,
It sounds like music,
In Joe Mercer's ear.
So come on and join us,
We're here to stay,
Come on with the Sky Blues,
As we all say!

We Know Who We Are

We know who we are,
We know who we are,
Champions of England,
We know who we are!

We Love You City

(To the tune of You Are My Sunshine)

We love you City, we do
We love you City, we do,
We love you City, we do
Oh City we love you!

(A firm favourite and a song that has been sung for decades)

Weaver, Nicky

Oh what a save,
Oh it's Nicky Weaver,
Oh what a save,
He's down to his left,
We went up…woooooh,
It's Nicky Weaver what a 'keeper,
What a save.

*(Unusual song for City's former No.1 with
a complete dance to accompany it)*

We'll Score Again...
(To the tune of We'll Meet Again)

We'll score again,
Don't know where, don't know when,
But I know we'll score again,
Some sunny day.

*(Sung during the darkest days of Stuart Pearce's reign when
City went an astonishing nine games without scoring a
Premier League goal at home)*

We'll Support You Evermore
(To the tune of Bread Of Heaven)

Man City, Man City,
We'll support,
We'll support,
We'll support you ever more!
We'll support you ever more!

*(Popular song sung when City are losing more
often than not!)*

We're Gonna Win The League

(To the tune of For He's A Jolly Good Fellow)

We're gonna win the league,
We're gonna win the league,
So now you gonna believe us?
So now you gonna believe us?
So now you gonna believe us?
We're gonna win the league!

*(Not heard for many years but sung at St James' Park after City
beat Newcastle 2-0 in the penultimate
game of the 2011/12 season)*

We're Not Really Here

(To the tune of We Shall Not Be Moved)

We are not, we're not really here,
We are not, we're not really here,
Like the friends of the Invisible Man,
We're not really here.

(There are more theories to this song than most, and anyone of them could be true. This song appears to have been inspired by City fans on tour in Ireland in the early 1990s who trashed the bar of the Metropole Hotel in Cork, then sung this impromptu song to the police officers sent to deal with the situation in the belief there was no proof as to which ones were responsible. It can't be ruled out! Whether that's true or not, we may never know, but the song really became popular on the terraces when the Blues slipped into the old Third Division for the first time in their history in the 1990s as an expression of bemusement at how a club of City's stature had managed to sink to an all-time low. Today, it is still sung with as much gusto at a packed City of Manchester Stadium as it was on the open terraces of places like Macclesfield Town and Lincoln City)

Whitley, Jeff
(To the tune of John Kettley Is A Weatherman)

Jeff Whitley is a clever man,
A clever man, a clever man,
Jeff Whitley is a clever man
And so is Stuart Pearce.

Wiekens, Gerard
(To the tune of Winter Wonderland)

There's only one, Gerard Wiekens,
One Gerard Wiekens,
We're walking along,
Singing this song,
Walking in a Wiekens wonderland!

WonderBall
(To the tune of Wonderwall)

And all the runs that Kinky makes are winding,
And all the goals that City score are blinding,
There are many times that we would like to score again,
But we don't know how,
'Cos maybe,
Eike's gonna be the one to save me (save me),
And after all,
You're my Alan Ball!

(Perhaps one of the most famous, if short-lived, of City songs. Adapted from the Oasis classic of the day, it actually serenaded manager Alan Ball who was in the process of taking the Blues down from the Premier League. However, the lyrics and tune were too good not to sing and the song was written about at length in the media)

Worst Support
(To the tune of Bread Of Heaven)

Worst support,
Worst support,
Worst support we've ever seen,
Worst support we've ever seen!

(Usually sung to any side with a quiet or sparse away following – as well as some home supporters on City's travels!)

Wright-Phillips, Shaun I
(To the tune of Hot, Hot, Hot!)

Shauny Wright-Wright-Wright,
Shauny Wright-Wright-Wright!

Wright-Phillips, Shaun II
(To the tune of Three Lions)

He's coming home,
He's coming home.
He's coming, Shauny's coming home!
He's coming home,
He's coming home,
He's coming, Shauny's coming home!

*(Sung when the news broke that Shaun Wright-Phillips
was about to re-sign for City in 2009)*

Yaya And Kolo
(To the tune of No Limits)

Yaya, Yaya-Yaya, Yaya-Yaya, Yaya, Yaya Toure.
Kolo, Kolo-Kolo, Kolo-Kolo, Kolo, Kolo Toure.

You Are My City
(To the tune of You Are My Sunshine)

You are my City, my only City,
You make me happy,
When skies are grey,
You'll never know just,
How much I love you,
So please don't take my City away.
Nah, nah, nah, nah-nah-ooh!

(A general uplifting song, usually heard when the team are playing well or are winning. Written in 1939, it has been around a long time and therefore difficult to pin a time down when it was first sung. Still popular and has stood the test of time)

66 Do I sing the songs in the shower? Maybe I have done once or twice! It is a source of great pride when the fans make a song about you – especially a good one – so it makes me very happy when I hear them sing my songs. 99

– Pablo Zabaleta

Zabaleta, Pablo I
(To the tune of Do The Conga)

Do, do, do,
Pablo Zabaleta,
Do, do, do,
Pablo Zabaleta!

*(The Argentinian man of steel has several songs in his honour but this one is
the most popular – to the Black Lace hit that also became
The Trainline's TV advert jingle)*

Zabaleta, Pablo II
(To the tune of Hey, Macarena!)

One Zaba,
Two Zaba,
Three Zabaleta.
Four Zaba,
Five Zaba,
Six Zabaleta.
Seven Zaba,
Eight Zaba,
Nine Zabaleta...
Hey, Zabaleta!

Zabaleta, Pablo III
(To the tune of I Am the Music Man)

Oh Pablo Zabaleta, he is a City man,
He plays for Argentina, he's harder than
Jaap Stam,
He plays in blue and white, for Pellegrini's men,
And when we win the league, we'll sing this
song again,
Oh....
Pablo Zabaleta, he is a City man,
He plays for Argentina, he's harder than
Jaap Stam,
He plays in blue and white, for Pellegrini's men,
And when we win the league, we'll sing this
song again!

*(What a way to finish – with perhaps the most popular
terrace chant of the last few years and another tribute to the
warrior that is Pablo Zabaleta)*

66 I'm still flabbergasted at the reception I receive each time and I still think, even today, that I have been a very lucky man. I've been lucky enough to play in front of the most magnificent fans in the world. **99**

– Bert Trautmann

Song Index

Index

S

Index

66 My happiness does not depend on if I am going to win all the titles or not. My question is: are the people who came to this game really enjoying it? Yes? Wow, that is enough. To win titles or not, we will see. 99

– Pep Guardiola

66 As a little kid in Bermuda, United was the team I wanted to play against because they were the team to beat. We held out comfortably to win 3-1 and I walked off to an incredible rendition of 'Feed The Goat' followed by 'Who Let The Goat Out?' Heaven! 99

– Shaun Goater

66 The fans are absolutely unbelievable at this club and I owe them so much. 99

– Georgi Kinkladze

66 It's flattering to think the club and fans have chosen 'Pounding' to help psyche the crowd up before games. I've been at the ground a few times when it's being played, but I stop short of tapping my foot to it – it's not the done thing! 99

– Andy Williams, Doves

MANCHESTER CITY SONGBOOK